THROUGH IT
ALL

ESTELLA WALKED WITH THE LORD

THROUGH IT ALL

ESTELLA WALKED WITH THE LORD

ZERA AMADI

ARPress

ILLUMINATING IDEAS.
EMPOWERING VOICES

ARPress
45 Dan Road Suite 5
Canton, MA 02021

Hotline: 1(888) 821-0229
Fax: 1(508) 545-7580

Ordering Information:

Quantity sales. Special discounts are available on quantity purchases by corporations, associations, and others. For details, contact the publisher at the address above.

Printed in the United States of America.

ISBN-13:	Softcover	979-8-89389-107-2
	eBook	979-8-89389-106-5

Library of Congress Control Number: 2024908838

CONTENTS

CHAPTER 1

ESTELLA'S JOURNEY

Estella found it difficult to part with her four children.

She loved her children very much and was prepared to go out of her way for their sake.

As a dedicated mother, Estella wanted her children to get education. She had just closed her school which she had opened after resigning from the college she was teaching. Estella wondered what step she was to take. It was not easy for Estella to go back to her employer to ask for a job, after deserting the school; because she had started her own school. Estella prayed and asked God to guide her in everything she was planning to do. Psalm 23:1 were one of the Bible verses that comforted Estella. She opened her Bible and read it aloud to her children, during their morning devotion.

The Lord is My Shepherd;

I Shall not want;

He makes me to lie down in green pastures

He leads me beside the still waters.

He restores my Soul;

He leads me in the way of righteousness for his
name – sake.

Even if I walk through the valley of the

Shadow of death,

I will fear no evil.

For you are with me, your rod and your staff, they
comfort me.

You prepare a table before me in the presence

of my enemies

You anoint my head with oil, my cup overflows

surely goodness and mercy shall follow me all

the days of my life and

I will live in the house of the Lord.

FOR EVER: AMEN

Nelly prayed to God to forgive them their sins and come to their rescue. Nelly prayed for God to open ways for their mother to be able to get a job or a business so that she could be able to feed, dress and pay school for them. Estella taught her children not to be ashamed of God; they should take the name of Jesus with them wherever they go. Jesus was to be their shield. Estella had dedicated her children to the Lord. Sunday was a day for everybody in Estella's house to go to church to worship God. Her two daughters got saved by accepting Jesus as their personal savior. Their mother worshiped in the Yearly Meeting of Friends; all her children joined the Kenya Assemblies of God. She did not stop them from worshiping with the Assemblies of God, because, when Estella was growing up Her grandma worshiped in the Assemblies of God. Estella carried a bucket of water for her grandma who smeared cow dung on the Church floor every Saturday. Grandma Ganigi volunteered to clean the church. Her grandmother carried cow dung. Estella felt it was quite in order for her children to worship where they found the Lord God. Estella's parents worshipped in the Salvation Army Church (Jeshi La Wokovu). Estella used to play the tambourine for the Church.

Estella cried every day to the Lord, to bless her with a job or a business to enable her to take care of her children, For there is a saying in Kiswahili which goes "Uchungu wa mwana ajuaye ni mzazi" "It is the parent that feels the Child's Pain." Estalla felt the pain of seeing her children at home without job opportunities. When you pray and believe in the Lord, mountains move and the earth, quakes. Estella and her children were prayer warriors. Their faith was very strong. Estella's mother was a strong prayer warrior like her.

It was on Monday morning when Estella went to the United States of America Embassy in Kenya, for a visa interview. Estella and her children woke up very early in the morning; on the material day to pray for visa provision. Her second born child prayed. This prayer was very strong. It gave Estella strength. Estella went to her appointment for her visa with a lot of confidence. The mercies of the Lord were with her. Estella arrived at the American embassy in good time, she found a very short line. Estella was number five on the line. The line moved very quickly, when she arrived at the building entrance, Estella was directed to sit in the waiting room. Estella sat in the waiting room patiently, people were called to different windows, but there was one immigration Officer, who was very harsh to people. When Estella saw, how he treated other people, she bowed her head and prayed to God to enable her, to be attended to by any other officer and not the harsh officer. God heard Estella's prayer and answered it immediately. When she opened her eyes, Estella heard her name. She was at first confused, she thought the harsh officer had called her but that was wrong, she was called to another window. Estella was very happy when she discovered that, God had answered her prayer, because she did not go to the man whom she referred to as "cruel" to the people, who went to his window to be granted visas to travel to the Land of opportunity. Estella went to the correct window she had prayed for. Estella had arranged all the required documents, which she gave to the immigration officer. The Officer looked at the documents Estella handed to him. He told Estella to go pay Ksh.150.00 to the last window. Estella thought she had not been issued the visa because they took her passport to the window. She went to pay, Estella paid the money and she was given a visa to travel to the Land of opportunity. Estella jumped with joy. She went to the road talking alone, she took a "Matatu" public transport home.

Estella was faced with one problem. After getting the visa to travel, Her problem was how to raise the air ticket. How and where was she going to get the air ticket? PSALM 121 – 1:2

I will lift up my eyes to the hills from where comes my help? My help comes from the Lord, who made heaven and earth; These verses were very comforting to Estella. She read them and prayed for the Lord God who created her, to take control of the situation. Estella knew her help was on the way. The help from the Lord.

When Estella finished praying God directed her on what to do. She had to think of her friends and relatives. God directed Estella to one of her relatives for help. Although Estella was shy to approach this relative to pay for her the ticket. She felt she was the only friend and relative who could help her. The lady had helped her before. Prayer is a very strong shield for a Christian. Prayer can move mountains and can make the earth to quake. God heard Estella's prayer. Prayer changes things. Those people who pray to God always, their prayers are answered. He will not allow your foot to be moved; He who keeps you will not slumber. Behold; He who keeps Israel shall neither slumber nor sleep. The Lord is your keeper; the Lord is your shade at your right hand. The sun shall not strike you by day, nor the moon by night. The Lord shall preserve you from all evil; He shall preserve your soul. The Lord shall preserve your going out and coming in from this time forth, and even forever more. These verses were read to Estella by her daughter Miriam, before she left for the Jomo Kenyatta International Airport Nairobi; Estella had arranged with her friend Jesca, her neighbor to take her to the airport to board the plane which was leaving at 11:30 pm.

Milkah her best friend came to escort her to the Jomo Kenyatta International Airport. Estella's two sons William and Jack accompanied her to the airport. Her two daughters could not escort their Mama because there was no room in the car. Miriam read Psalm 121: 1-8 and then Nelly prayed for her mother for journey mercies. Jesca came at 10 pm, Estella was not happy, because she did not know how the four children were going to survive. They were lucky their father had bought a small house in Buruburu; so they were not going to pay rent.

All they needed was money for food. At the back of the house there was a one bedroomed extension{studio}; which they had rented out; it was a substitute for bills like electricity, garbage and security. He will not allow your foot to be moved. He who keeps you will not slumber; Behold he who keeps Israel shall neither slumber nor sleep. The Lord is your keeper at your right hand. Estella believed that her children will not suffer. They will be taken care of by God the father; Estella arrived at the Jomo Kenyatta International Airport and was directed to where she was to wait for the flight. While she was waiting for her flight after checking in; Estella sat next to another woman, whom she greeted with a smile. The lady responded to Estella's greeting. As they sat waiting for their flight Estella asked the woman if she was traveling to America. The woman told Estella that she was traveling to Canada for a meeting (conference). Estella told her she was traveling to the United States of America (USA). The woman told Estella, they will part at the Heathrow London Airport. After a few minutes they announced that their airplane was ready. They took their hand luggage and hurried to board the plane. Unfortunately, they sat in different seats. But when the plane landed at Heathrow Airport, Estella and her friend went to sit in the hotel or restaurant while waiting for the flight.

At the restaurant Estella's new friend ordered two cups of tea. London was very cold. The hot cup of tea was to warm them a little. When the friend of Estella was ordering tea, Estella told her she will not be able to pay for her cup of tea because she had no money at all. But the friend assured her that she will pay for the two cups of tea and the snacks. The waiter served them with tea and a snack, Estella thanked her friend. As they were taking tea, Estella's friend asked her if she had a husband. Estella responded very quickly to the friend. She said, yes and No, her husband was alive but he decided to separate; he went to the village and warned Estella not to step there. The man said Estella was an embarrassment to him, just because Estella liked wearing long pants (trousers).

According to Estella's husband, women who put on trousers are prostitutes. Estella's friend was very sorry for her. Estella told her that she depended on the little money which the tenant, who had rented her extension, was paying. It was not a lot of money, but Estella managed. Her friend was very sorry for Estella. On one hand she understood what Men are capable of doing to their wives but Estella's husband was the most different. Estella, do you know anybody where you are going? She asked; Estella told her that her friend went there ahead of her, so she was hoping she would meet her at the airport. So what are you going there for? She asked Estella. Estella told her she was going to attend a meeting or conference. Estella asked her friend how about you? Are you visiting someone in Canada? She told her, she was a university professor, she was going to a seminar for a year. Wow: Estella was surprised, and how about your children and their father? She told Estella, her husband died two years ago. She was left with her three children, two boys and a daughter. All the three children were adults with jobs. Estella congratulated her. As they were resting after a cup of tea, Estella's friend opened her handbag and gave Estella $50.00. Estella was almost kneeling, but she stopped Estella from kneeling for her. Estella thanked her dearly. She was happy that she at least had some little money to put in her handbag. She was very happy indeed, God almighty had remembered her as soon as they finished taking their cup of tea, there was announcement, that Estella's flight was ready. Agnes Estella's friend escorted her to where she was to enter her flight. Agnes and Estella hugged each other bye, and Estela entered the airplane full of tears in her eyes. She thanked her friend Agnes; she wished her all the best. Estella sat next to a white woman from Heathrow London Airport to Michigan, the plane did not take long, they arrived in Detroit when it was 20 minutes to the landing time, the Air hostess announced that people should buckle their safety belts, because the plane will be landing. The pilot in control thanked all the passengers, Estella talked to God again; to at least let her friend come to meet her at the airport for she had nobody else, to meet her, Estella followed the other passengers, she reached where, she was to pick up her old-fashioned suitcase, she had borrowed from her brother. Estella picked her suitcase and joined the other people. Estella reached the immigration office. She stood on the visitor's line. The immigration Officer checked her passport. The officer asked Estella where she was going, she said she was going for a women's conference. The officer asked Estella to go ahead. On reaching out she looked around and saw her friend Esther. She came and hugged her. She introduced her to her friend who had escorted her to the airport. "The sun shall not strike you by day nor the moon by the night. The Lord shall preserve you from all evil He shall preserve your soul."

CHAPTER 2

LIFE IN UNITED STATES OF AMERICA

Estella arrived in the United States of America safely. She was welcomed and taken to the house, where she was hosted for only two days. The third day the owner of the house could not accommodate four grown women in her house, it was too expensive for her, so she asked if the two black women could seek another suitable accommodation. Estella went to the room where she slept the night before and prayed to God the Father to prepare another accommodation for her. Estella was in the wilderness Where does she go? She asked God. God loves us very much and he is always ready and willing to answer our prayer requests. God responded to Estella's prayer requests. In a few minutes, two women came to greet the international visitors, one was white and the other was African American. They greeted the visitors, the African American talked to the host and asked her if she could take two women to her house to host them. The host told her to take the two African women. The African American was driving a Dodge Durango.

Estella and Esther went with the fellow black woman. When they were still on the way to her home. Their new host told the two women that her husband died, her children were grown and living with their families. She was left alone. It was her wish, if she could have a companion. Estella was very happy to hear what the woman had said; Esther whispered to Estella "You have a temporary job." Esther answered Dr. Rhonda, "Oh, Estella can help you for some time. Rhonda was a doctor." Dr. Rhonda was happy to hear that Estella was remaining with her. She told Esther, "Yes." She will remain with me. In a few minutes, they arrived at the woman's house well fenced. Dr. Rhonda opened her door and welcomed the two guests into her house. She gave them some cold juice. After the juice, Dr. Rhonda asked Estella to start her new job. She promised Esther that she will be paying Estella $100.00 every month.

When the two ladies changed the one hundred dollars into their currency, it added to Ksh.10,000. They felt it was on the lower side for her. Estella started working, she started by picking the clothes which were on the floor at the laundry place, she had never seen a laundry machine; it was her first time to see it. She asked Dr. Rhonda to show her how to operate the laundry machines. Dr. Rhonda was more than happy to show her how to operate both washing machine and drying machine. Estella started washing the dirty clothes which she found in the laundry room. While the washing machine was running, Estella was shown where she could pick some clothes for washing. When she came back to the laundry, the clothes which were in the washing machine were ready to be put in the drying machine. She put the wet clothes in the drying machine, while the second lot of clothes were drying. Estella started folding the clothes which could not be ironed, and the ones which were to be ironed, Estella ironed them. Rhonda gave her some new suitcases where she was to put the ironed clothes. All the three suitcases were full. Rhonda told her to put the bed sheets in one box without mixing them. Estella followed the instructions on how to pack the clothes all the packed clothes and bed sheets were given to her friend Esther to take them with her to Africa.

Esther was going back to Africa. The following day, Rhonda advised her that it was good, if they could take her luggage to the airport in the evening, it was easy for her to only remain with the hand luggage on the day of traveling. They took all the three suitcases to the airport. The boxes were weighted and she was given the receipt which she carried to the airport the following day. It was time for Esther to travel to Africa. Dr. Rhonda and Estella escorted her to the airport. Estella was very sad to part with her friend Esther. She could not control her tears which rolled along her cheeks, she wiped them very fast, but the mucus filled her nose. Estella was shy pushing the mucus back to her nose. Instead of flushing them in a handkerchief which she did not have when they went back to the car, Dr. Rhonda gave her some Kleenex to blow her nose. She felt good because the mucus stopped embarrassing her. They went up to the restaurant to have lunch. When time came to order their meal. Estella did not know the names of food, the names were quite different from what she knew; Estella had learned British English which was a little different from American English. Estella asked Dr. Rhonda to order food for her. She will be able to order for herself when she learns the names of foods. Rhonda ordered their food. She ordered for Estella a plate of French fries and one big chicken leg with soda. Estella enjoyed the food they ate while chatting. Rhonda asked her some questions if she had children. Estella told her that she had four children, two girls and two boys, the two women shared a lot.

The two women had their dinner at the restaurant and were quite satisfied. When they arrived home, they did not cook. Estella had washed all the dirty linen. The two women had a lot to share, they sat in the living room, watching television, they continued to share. Rhonda was very interested in knowing Estella. They sat until 9pm then they went to bed. Estella was given the basement to sleep. Estella had never seen a basement; it was her first time to experience a basement. But she was happy to live in the basement.

CHAPTER 3

Estella was grateful to be given accommodation by Rhonda. She had a very large basement to herself. In the basement, there was a refrigerator, and a stove which she was not using because she was eating what Rhonda was making. If Dr. Rhonda did not cook Estella would not eat. She depended very much on Ronda for everything. Estella continued housekeeping for Rhonda. Estella was to wake up at 5 am, go to the shower after dressing. Estella went upstairs to clean the rooms, after cleaning upstairs, Estella was taken to Rhonda's school of nursing to clean the classrooms. The largest was the church which was very big. They used the church too. Dr. Rhonda's school started with students who were taking CNA and Anatomy and Physiology. It was too much for Estella, who was 48 years old. Estella cleaned the classroom and Rhonda's home. Estella never had lunch, she only had breakfast and sometimes Estella would eat dinner but the most important thing was accommodation, she did not worry about food. Accommodation for Estella was very essential whenever she felt hungry, Estella would drink some water. It was not everyday that Estella missed eating, she would miss once or twice a week. One morning,

Rhonda's sister who was one of the teachers in the school, asked Estella to dress up and go to school with her. Her name was Dr. Bella. Estella was afraid, Estella told her that she was afraid because Dr. Rhonda had not given her permission to join the school but Dr. Bella told Estella that she knew her sister. Estella had no other choice but to dress up and follow Dr. Bella.

Dr. Bella drove up to a certain store where she bought Estella's classroom material, which were pencils, folders, and foolscap papers. Estella was grateful when they reached the school. She was given textbooks, a kind student bought Estella a bag for her books. Estella was introduced to the other students in class. The students were very happy to welcome Estella as a new member of their school. They were excited to meet Estella from Africa wearing clothes. They asked Estella many questions about Africa. One of the students asked her, how she got clothes. Estella smiled and told her, Dr. Rhonda bought her the clothes and taught her how to wear them; otherwise she was naked when she arrived at the airport. They all laughed, another student asked Estella that she heard, "Africans do not have houses, so where do they sleep?" Estella smiled and told her, some Africans sleep on trees. Others live in caves, "What do Africans eat?" One of the students asked. They eat fish and fruits but some eat beef, and fresh blood from the cows. All the students were very happy. Estella told one of the students, that she would have wanted her to marry her son, but she wonders how she will transport cows from Africa to the United States of America for her dowry. The whole class asked Estella what dowry was.

Estella explained to them, that is what parents of the man give to the parents of the girl as an appreciation. "So you sell your daughters to men." "No" said Estella, "It is an appreciation to the parents of the girl." Estella had many questions to answer. Estella settled in one of the classrooms Dr. Bella showed her. The first teacher to teach the first lesson was Dr. Rhonda, she taught Anatomy and Physiology. Dr. Rhonda was a Registered Nurse, but she had a doctorate in Divinity and her sister Dr. Bella had a doctorate in Education or something of the sort. After the lesson all her classmates asked Estella how she knew how to write, read and speak English. Estella explained to the students how she knew the English language. She told them that, when she was in Africa, she had not known how to speak and write English, but Dr. Rhonda quickly taught her how to read, write and speak English while at the airport. They told her, then she must be a very bright student to learn a language in a few minutes. They asked Estella another question, which made Estella to laugh. "Do you have cars, trains, and Aeroplanes in Africa?" Estella told them that people in Africa just walk and run, they run as fast as a cheetah, there are no vehicles of any form. Estella told them that while she was running, the "pilot" saw her running and he landed to pick her. After picking her, she asked about her destination. Estella told the pilot she wanted to go to the United States of America and that was how she landed in America: "Oh it was quite interesting," Some sympathized with her while others laughed at poor Estella. Estella found very interesting friends, they were very good young people. Some brought different fruits for Estella. Estella sat in a class of CNA, when she finished she moved to the

Anatomy and Physiology 2. She passed Anatomy 1 and 2 then proceeded to an LPN class. Estella by the help of the other students managed to understand the training.

The lord shall preserve you from all evil. He shall preserve your soul. As the word of God tells us, it is true, God preserved Estella from all evil. It was one morning at around 4 am, Dr. Rhonda was throwing things upstairs. The noise woke Estella from sleep. Estella wondered what might be happening. She ran upstairs very fast to go and see what was happening to her employer, and great Mama. When Dr. Rhonda set her eyes on Estella, she started screaming and cursing Estella. The poor woman was flabbergasted Because she had never encountered such an action from Dr. Rhonda whom she respected very much. Estella started crying and asked her what she had done wrong. Estella pleaded with her to pardon her, if she had done anything wrong to her. Dr. Rhonda eventually asked her to leave her house. This scared Estella very much. Estella being a dedicated Christian, went down to the basement and went down on her knees to pray. Estella asked God the Father to talk to Dr. Rhonda to calm down and forgive Estella. God spoke to Estella, and told her to go back to Dr. Rhonda and ask her to let her finish her LPN course. But everything fell on a hard rock. Dr. Rhonda refused the last word, God told Estella to pack all her belongings, and leave her premises. When Dr. Rhonda was going to work, she told Estella that she should not get her in her house. Estella went back to the basement and prayed again. She told God, that Dr. Rhonda had refused. God told Estella to pack all her belongings, and she should not take anything that belonged to Dr. Rhonda.

Estella did what God told her. She packed all her clothes in the old suitcase she came with from Kenya. She found herself stranded. She did not know where to go at all. She carried her clothes, which she packed in the suitcase and trash bags to the staircase. She sat on the steps and told God "God my father you asked me to pack my belongings. I have packed, but I do not know what to do next." God instructed her to call Pastor Frank, she called Pastor Frank and just told him, "Pastor, can you please give me sister Anita's number?" Pastor did not hesitate. He gave her the number immediately. Estella called sister Anita, she just told her sister, "Sister Anita please help me. Dr. Rhonda has asked me to leave her residence and I have nowhere to go. Please help me." Sister Anita did not hesitate, she came immediately. Sister Anita asked Estella to carry everything of hers. She should not leave anything behind. They parked the belongings of Estella in sister Anita's van and left for sister Anita's house, on their way, sister Anita stopped at a restaurant. Sister Anita ordered some food, she asked Estella to order her food, she ordered food; French fries and chicken. The waiter served Estella French fries full on a wide plate and two big legs of chicken. Estella having been hungry for several days ate the food very fast. Sister Anita asked if she needed more food, but she said she was alright. The two women proceeded to sister Anita's house. At the house, there was a very beautiful young female dog, named Sugar. She was a very friendly dog. This dog behaved as if she knew Estella's problems. She kept checking on Estella most of the time, in the room, Estella was sleeping. Estella was at sister Anita's house.

Estella left for New Jersey after two days. Estella met another young woman from home who hosted Estella, she was to share a bed with her mother, Estella had it rough. She was scolded by this Mama every morning, telling Estella that she was going to break her daughter's expensive bed. She asked Estella if she came all the way to America to come and be a burden to her daughter. Estella would only smile and give her "no" as an answer. Estella tried hard to get contact of different people from her country who were in the United States of America. Estella eventually got some contact of one of the country people. She kept calling the young girl everyday asking for help, the lady would tell her to be patient. Estella was patient enough, but she did not forget to ask God all the time to remember her. Estella believed in God and she trusted that God was going to answer her prayer. God can never leave you, if you pray and trust in Him. As the song goes "trust and obey; for there is no other way to be happy in Jesus, but only to trust Him, and obey." One day when Estella was not expecting any call, she heard her telephone ring, she grabbed the phone and Melap was calling her to let her know that she could go to Pennsylvania. She had found some good accommodation for her. Estella was so happy to hear that accommodation had been found. Estella knelt down and prayed, thanking Him for Melap and what she had done for her. Melap had talked to another lady who had a two-bedroom house. She agreed to share her house with Estella. She managed to get one week every month for Estella to work. Estella's nephew drove her to Pennsylvania. When Estella arrived, Melap took her to the house. The lady welcomed Estella wholeheartedly and offered her a bed, well furnished. The following day, Estella was taken to where she was to work. Estella found the job easy because she had just graduated from the certified nurse assistant class. Estella enjoyed working, she was taking care of one gentleman.

Surely Goodness and Mercy shall follow me all the days of my life:

One Monday morning, Estella picked the newspapers and started reading. She came across an advertisement; they wanted a caregiver to take care of an old woman. Estella took the telephone and made a call to the agency which had put the advertisement in the papers. Immediately some gentleman picked the call and answered. Estella went straight to the point, she was a trained and experienced caregiver. Estella was invited for an interview. She filled the forms, she was asked some questions. Estella was told the main interview which was to determine if she was going to be taken or not was at the house where this Mama was, when they arrived at her house, her children were having some breakfast. Estella and the interviewer entered the house. They were welcomed to sit. As they sat, there was an empty chair close to where Estella sat. One of the young men at the kitchen table went upstairs and came with a very smart old lady. Her name was Evelyn. She sat on the chair next to Estella. The daughter served Evelyn a cup of coffee. The family was very happy because their mother smiled when she saw Estella. Estella was friendly to her and they started talking to each other. Estella was given the job, she had passed the interview.

PSALM 20

May the Lord answer you in the day of trouble; May the name of the God of Jacob defend you; May he send help from the sanctuary, and strengthen you out of Zion;

God answered Estella, when she felt she was in trouble. The name of the God of Jacob defended Estella, when she was told she had passed her interview and was asked to start work as soon as possible.

CHAPTER 4

May he send you help from the sanctuary, and strengthen you out of Zion. God sent Estella help and made her strong. The Lord gave Estella a job of her own. She was no longer working for one week. She had her own job which she was proud to say it was her full time job. When Estella worked the first week in the job, she was given a check of $700. Estella had no bank account at all. Her friend took her check and cashed for her. Estella opened her account where she could bank or deposit her own checks. God strengthened Estella, by offering her a job and enabling her to open her own bank account. Estella found it easier to cash her check when she was paid at her new job. Estella got a "live in" position where she was to work for seven days. Estella was paid every week, she made $100 per day, since she had two clients. For the two clients, Estella was making $200 per day. She was able to earn $1400 every week. These money was very helpful because, Estella sent to her children to pay their school fees. God protected Estella's children from drugs and any other bad things that could destruct them from their education.

JOB – 21 – 22

"And he said; Naked I came from my mother's womb, and naked shall I return there. The Lord gave, and the Lord has taken away; Blessed be the name of the Lord. In all this job did not sin nor charge God with wrong. After barely a month Estella lost one of her clients. Estella felt very sorry, but she was left with one client, whom she cared for. One year when the client died, Estella cried very much because she was very much attached to the client.

Estella felt as if her own Mother had died. But "God gave and God took." God took what belonged to him, Estella cried, but asked God for forgiveness. Life had to continue. Estella had to pack her goods, and leave the premises because her job had come to an end. Despite her being with the job, Mama Evelyn was a mother she loved. Having been the first person she took care of, Estella was affected very much. But it is well, it is well. Estella loved the family of Evelyn very much. They too loved her. One of Evelyn's children found another job for Estella. She went to take care of another senior citizen who was 90 years old. Estella was very comfortable taking care of senior citizens. They bonded well. It was barely three months after accepting to care for Linda, when Estella received news from Africa that her mother had died. Estella mourned her mother. Linda asked her to take some days from work to go and mourn her mother. While at home, Estella received a call from some lady by name Marjorie offering her another job opportunity. Estella was to go and work in a group home setup. Estella had to care for bedridden women and one man who had dementia. Estella gave the job she had of caring for Linda to her roommate. She was to take over from Estella. The group home was full of senior citizens who were not able to walk on their own. They needed a lot of assistance. Estella managed because she loved her job. She was to live there. She shared a room with Roxa who was 99 years old. Estella liked Roxa. It was a live in position. Estella was working alone from Sunday to Sunday. It was too much for her, she had to request two days off, that is Saturday and Sunday. The boss agreed at least, Estella was able to rest. She later booked an air ticket and was able to travel to Africa to put flowers on her Mama's grave. "It is well, it is well" "Naked I came from my Mother's womb, and naked I shall return there. The Lord gave and Lord has taken away; Blessed be the name of the Lord." Estella believed her Mother was in greater peace. Life had to go on. She was to continue. Estella came back to the USA and continued with her job. Estella applied in a school where she was admitted. She continued to work hard in school and graduated with her degree. Estella has been very grateful to the United States of America. Estella managed to take her four children to school. God provided Estella's children with some education. She never ceased to pray to God Almighty and thank Him for all He did for her. Estella thanks America and asks God to bless America.

Estella met new friends who were very good to her, her fellow students and teachers all wanted Estella to succeed. There were times Estella was not able to understand some teachers, but the other students would explain to her. Estella always remembers Dr. Rhonda who hosted her for almost a year. Estella understands that it is not easy to host someone you have no clue at all, more so from another continent. God bless Dr. Rhonda who regret parting ways with Estella.

CHAPTER 5

When God blesses you, nobody can be against it. His blessings are final. If God wants one to eat, dress and live well it will come to pass. Estella managed to live and work in the United States of America. Estella had wanted in her life to drive a car of her own. God blessed Estella with a car. Estella managed to pass her driving test and became a driver. God is great.

Lamentations: 3 – 21 – 26

This I recall to my mind, therefore I have hope. Through the Lord's mercies we are not consumed because His compassions fail not. They are new every morning, great is your faithfulness.

The Lord is my portion says my soul therefore I hope in him. The Lord is good to those who wait for Him to the soul who seeks Him.

Estella was very grateful to God Almighty who provided for Estella when she prayed unto him. "A thousand years is like one day to God." When God remembers one, everything the person went through is forgotten, all problems pass like a cloud. When Estella was in her country, she did not know that through her hard work, she could be a mother to a film producer/journalist, a medical doctor, a graphic designer and a lawyer. God is a miraculous God, when he wants to help he means business. Estella says she cannot thank God enough. Nelly who is the first born child of Estella and now Dr. Nelly was a very responsible person. She persuaded her siblings to be serious with their education for their Mother was struggling in the U.S.A to give them school fees. They should be able to show their Mom certificates. They worked hard. The graphic designer finished his school early and was able to get a job. He became very helpful to the family. Nelly went to Kampala University in Uganda. When she finished her higher diploma in clinic medicine, she was not able to be employed in Kenya so she had to take another year at the Kenya Medical school in order to pass the exams for her to be employed. She worked hard and within a year she had achieved the required grade, she was posted in one of the hospitals in the country.

PHILIPPIANS 4:13

I CAN DO ALL THINGS THROUGH HIM WHO GIVES ME STRENGTH

When the Lord is on your side and you trust in him. Everything that you do or plan to do God gives you courage and strength to do it. You can do all that you plan to do through Jesus Christ our Lord who will give you the strength. In the Old Testament, the son of David Solomon, God gave him wisdom, to help him rule. He asked God for the wisdom, whatever you ask God, He will provide. Estella prayed to God for provision and God granted her.

TIMOTHY : 3: 15 – 16

And that from childhood you have known the Holy scriptures which we are able to make you wise for salvation through faith which is in Christ Jesus. All scripture is given by inspiration of God and is profitable for doctrine, for reproof, for correction, for instruction in righteousness.

The Lord gave Estella strength and wisdom which helped her to achieve her goal. Estella's goal was to travel to the land of opportunity in order to care for her children. Estella was able to feed and educate her children. Estella still prays for the land and nation of USA without forgetting her Mother land Africa.

PSALMS: 32: 7-10

You are my hiding place: You shall preserve me from trouble; You shall surround me with songs of deliverance. I will instruct you and teach you in the way you should go, I will guide you with my eye. God was always with Estella and her children. God also worked with Jared the father of Estella's children. When he deserted Estella and their children and went to live in the village alone.

Jared went ahead and divorced Estella, just because she was hustling for her children. Estella did not hate him at all. She continued praying for him but God is the one who knows our future. When his son was graduating from the university, Jared came from the village to celebrate with his son. He was very happy. Jared learned that the other kids had finished their school and were working. When he reached the village after attending his son's achievements, he called Estella and thanked her very much. This is what he told his ex-wife. "Thank you very much for taking shame out of me, you have made me a proud father whom I thought I wouldn't be." Estella being a devoted Christian recalled the Lord's prayer "Father forgive those who trespass against us and lead us not into temptation but deliver us from evil" Estella thought, "if she always ask God to forgive her, then she should first of all forgive those who wrong her, so that God can deliver her from all evil. Estella forgave her ex-husband." Jared did not live long. He became very sick and he left the world. He died because he did not have proper care. The caregiver he employed learned that the old man had divorced his wife and had not remarried. Jared's children would only visit him during the weekend. The caregiver left him to die hoping to inherit his property. The caregiver ended up in a fiasco. Jared had given one of his sons his identity card to keep for him in Nairobi. But he did not tell his son the reason for giving him the identity card. When he died, the children were able to freeze their Father's bank account.

When the caregiver went to the ATM to take money, he was blocked. God is our hiding place; he preserves us from trouble, He can surround us with deliverance songs. God taught Estella's kids what they were to do. He preserved their father's property from the caregiver who went to the bank and told them that Jared's kids were useless. He guided them with his eyes. Estella is always thanking God for all that he has done for her. God is our father who loves us despite our sins, even after hanging his son on the cross, He still loves us. Thank you, God.

Through it all, Estella walked with the Lord. She still walks with the Lord to this time, she walked a walk. Jesus never left Estella. Nelly promised her mother that she would pay for her school fees to upgrade her career. Nelly managed to get a job as a clinical officer in one of the counties in Kenya. She worked hard and she joined the university to study for a bachelor's degree in clinical medicine, she graduated. After graduation, the young girl continued with her education to a masters degree in Biochemistry and Biology, so she did Biostatistics. She qualified as a doctor. Hard work pays, hard work with prayers, they make a big difference. Nelly kept on asking her two brothers and sister to pursue their education. Her brother who is a lawyer decided to go for his masters degree. God was with Estella and her children. Estella is a prayerful woman, she believes and trust in the Lord Almighty. The film producer decided to do a bachelor's degree in business administration. God is a wonderful God. Through it, Estella walked with the Lord, she is a Christian who still walks in the Lord. Estella is always grateful to the Lady who took her to her house and took care of her. She has prayed for this mother she found in America. God bless her.

It is not easy to settle in a strange land. The green card does not grant you a job. It does not give you accommodation. Green card does not offer clothing at all. You get a green card and be prepared to find a job for yourself, get your own accommodation, it can even be worse when you come with children. While away, one thinks life with a green card is easy. But for the hardworking person, you can enjoy afterwards. No easy task so to speak. Estella is grateful to everyone who assisted her when she stepped on the USA soil. To God be the Glory. Through it all, Estella never forgot God.